Topic 1

Globalisation and trade

Causes and effects of globalisation

The term 'globalisation' has been used widely since the 1990s, but the idea has been around for centuries. The world economy became much more integrated during the nineteenth century, but trade and capital flows fell during the Great Depression and the Second World War, and then globalisation increased again afterwards. The IMF defines globalisation as 'the process through which an increasingly free flow of ideas, people, goods, services and capital leads to the integration of economies and societies'. For example, firms like Apple have off-shored production to Foxconn in China.

Recession in the world economy following the 2008 financial crisis, and subsequent policy responses to strengthen regulations and domestic markets, have led some to refer to this trend as deglobalisation.

---

1 **Identify two characteristics of deglobalisation. (AO1)**   2 marks

....

....

2 **Explain the role the IMF, the World Bank or the WTO has played in promoting globalisation. (AO1, AO2, AO3)**   5 marks

....

....

....

....

....

3 **Examine TWO factors which led to increased globalisation before the global financial crisis in 2008. (AO1, AO2, AO3, AO4)**   8 marks

....

....

....

....

....

....

....

4 **Discuss whether the positive effects of globalisation outweigh the negatives. (AO1, AO2, AO3, AO4)**   15 marks

Write your answer on a separate sheet of paper.

Comparative advantage and the terms of trade

David Ricardo's theory of comparative advantage is the principal theory that supports free trade. According to the theory, specialisation and free trade will increase total output and economic welfare even if the country you are trading with has an absolute advantage. For the gains of comparative advantage to be enjoyed by both countries, certain assumptions have to be made — there must also be different opportunity cost ratios and an acceptable rate of exchange agreed of one product for another (terms of trade).

5 Define the following two terms:

a **comparative advantage (AO1)**   `2 marks`

....

....

b **absolute advantage (AO1)**   `2 marks`

....

....

6 Based on the following information, when each country devotes half of its resources to the production of cars and half to computers, answer the questions that follow.

Country	Cars	Computers
UK	200	600
China	300	1,500
Total pre-trade		

a Complete the table to show the total output of cars and computers before trade. (AO2)   `1 mark`

b Which country has the absolute advantage in making cars and making computers? (AO2)   `1 mark`

....

c Calculate the following opportunity costs. (AO2)   `2 marks`

Country	Opportunity cost of producing 1 car	Opportunity cost of producing 1 computer
UK		
China		

d Complete the table after specialisation and trade. (AO1, AO2, AO3) `4 marks`

Country	Cars	Computers
UK		0
China	100	
Total post-trade		

e   Define 'terms of trade'. (AO1)   `2 marks`

....

f   Choose the terms of trade, or rate of exchange (after the specialisation in part d), that
    would benefit both countries and so lead to a higher combined total output than
    before free trade. (AO1, AO2, AO3)   `4 marks`

Country	Cars	Computers
UK		
China		
Total post-trade		

Read the following stimulus material and answer the questions that follow.

Terms of trade shift

China's import prices have, on balance, risen more than its export prices, contributing to a deterioration in its terms of trade
(the price of its imports relative to imports).

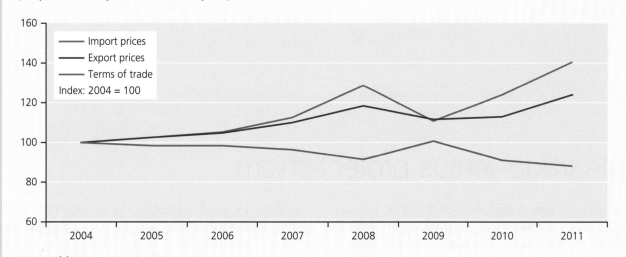

Figure 1 (a) Terms of trade, 2004–11

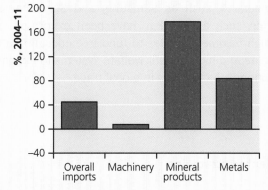

Figure 1 (b) Import price growth

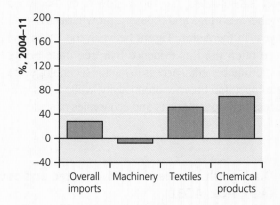

Figure 1 (c) Export price growth

Source: IMF (**www.tinyurl.com/z89j7u8**)

7 With reference to Figure 1, explain what could have caused an improvement in the terms of trade. (AO1, AO2, AO3) 5 marks

....

....

....

....

8 With reference to Figure 1, explain ONE positive and ONE negative effect of an improvement in the terms of trade. (AO1, AO2, AO3) 5 marks

....

....

....

....

9 Explain why the assumptions underlying the theory of comparative advantage might make free trade less beneficial than it may appear. (AO1, AO2, AO3) 5 marks

....

....

....

....

Free trade versus protectionism

Since Ricardo proved that free trade would increase welfare, most countries today are members of the WTO and believe that **outward-oriented** growth, and so export promotion, is superior to **inward-orientated** strategies, or import substitution. The rapid growth of the world economy between 1945 and 2008, and growth rates of over 7% per year in the **Asian Tigers** between the 1960s and 1990s, are often used as evidence that free trade brings many important benefits. Access to foreign technology and greater competition improve productivity, while firms gain from accessing larger markets and economies of scale.

The difficulty lies in balancing the benefits from trade and minimising the disadvantages from a possible loss of infant industries and overspecialisation in sectors with little potential for innovation. For example, the government in South Korea initially protected large conglomerates, such as Samsung, and Scandinavian countries, such as Sweden, have been export-led yet used high income tax rates to fund free education and healthcare and high-benefit welfare systems to mitigate the economic fluctuations in global trade.

10 Distinguish between inward-oriented and outward-oriented strategies. (AO1, AO2, AO3) 5 marks

....

....

....

....

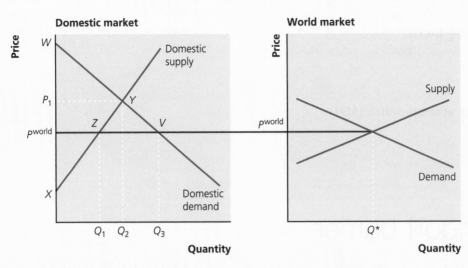

Figure 2 Domestic and world markets

⑪ Figure 2 shows the world market for one product compared to an individual country's market for that same product. Price is determined in the world market and is lower than in the domestic (individual country) market. Complete the table below. (AO1) `4 marks`

Domestic market	Consumers	Domestic firms
Quantity demanded or supplied		
Area of consumer or producer surplus		

⑫ Apart from comparative advantage and the gains for consumers, explain TWO other advantages of opening up to free trade. (AO1, AO2) `4 marks`

....

....

....

....

⑬ Explain each of the following reasons for protectionism:

a infant industry argument (AO1) `2 marks`

....

....

b job protection (AO1) `2 marks`

....

....

c to prevent dumping (AO1)

2 marks

....

....

d to correct current account deficit (AO1)

2 marks

....

....

Types of import barrier

Countries can protect themselves against imports through a variety of different measures. Since China joined the WTO in 2001, US exports to China have grown by over 500% but the USA's bilateral trade deficit has also reached record levels. China is accused of unfairly subsidising its exports and the USA has filed WTO cases against China in industries including auto parts, rare earths and credit card payments.

Since the global financial crisis, governments have felt justified in trying to support struggling domestic firms, initially through non-tariff measures but also through emergency tariffs or countervailing duties on imports deemed to be subsidised by foreign governments. The alleged use of 'beggar-thy-neighbour' policies, like officially induced exchange depreciation, risks retaliation and a fall in international trade.

⑭ Define, and give an example of, the following terms: (AO1, AO2)

8 marks

Term	Definition	Example
Tariff		
Quota		
Non-tariff measures		
Subsidies to domestic producers		

⑮ With the use of a tariff diagram, evaluate the economic impact of the introduction of a tariff. (AO1, AO2, AO3, AO4)

12 marks

....
....
....
....

16 **Evaluate the impact on the global economy of a significant increase in protectionist measures. (AO1, AO2, AO3, AO4)**   **25 marks**

Use the table below to help you plan your answer, and then write your essay on a separate sheet of paper. Aim to include at least three analysis and evaluation points.

Point/knowledge (AO1 4 marks)	Analysis (AO3 8 marks)	Application (AO2 4 marks)	Evaluation (AO4 9 marks)
Read the question; make sure your points are relevant; define economic concepts	Use of economic concepts; explained, annotated and labelled diagrams; use of logical chains of reasoning	Integrated supporting evidence from the extract, your own examples and the context of the question	Arguments for and against; significance of arguments; reference to context and evidence; a justified conclusion that considers the question as a whole, not just one part

Patterns of trade, trade blocs and the role of the WTO

World trade grew faster than world GDP, particularly after 1990: merchandise trade grew at an average rate of 5.3% from 1992 to 2012 and at a pre-crisis average rate of 6.0% (1990–2008). The growth of trade was significantly higher in China and India than globally and in OECD countries.

This rapid growth in trade was matched by a shift in market shares in world trade from advanced economies towards some emerging economies. Between 1985 and 2008, China's share in world exports of goods increased from 2% to nearly 10% and India's market share doubled, though from low initial levels, whereas the share more than halved in some OECD countries (e.g. Japan and the UK).

One major event contributing to the rapid increase in trade during the last decade was the opening up of China's market to international trade following its WTO membership in 2001. Another factor was the geographical fragmentation of production chains with increased sourcing of foreign intermediate inputs.

9

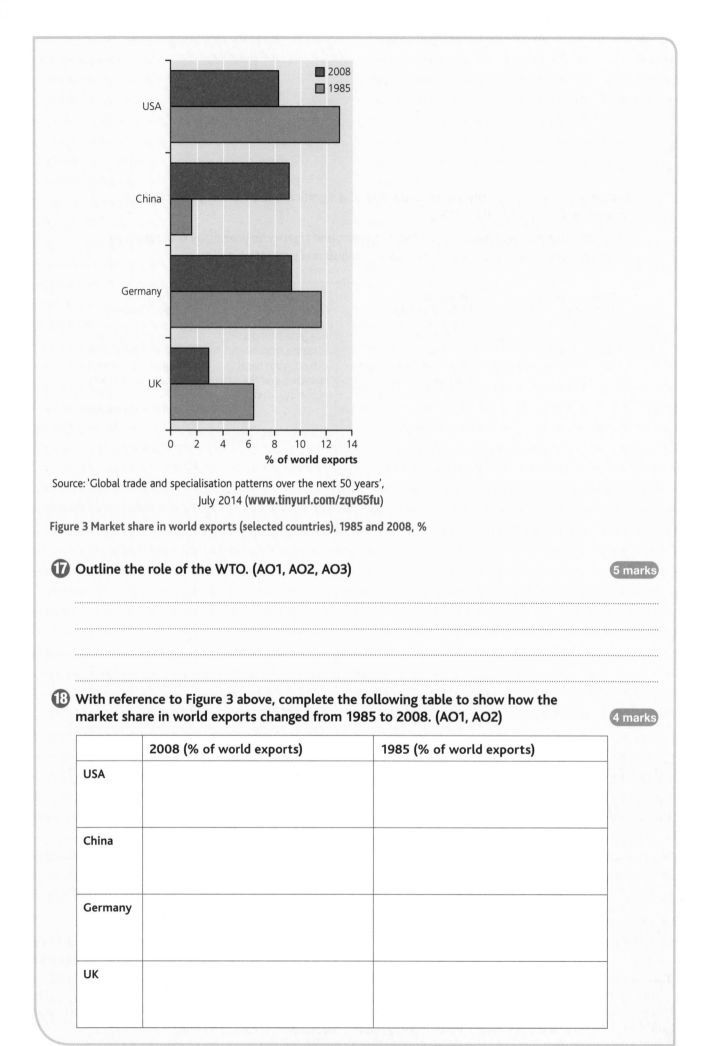

Source: 'Global trade and specialisation patterns over the next 50 years',
July 2014 (**www.tinyurl.com/zqv65fu**)

Figure 3 Market share in world exports (selected countries), 1985 and 2008, %

17 Outline the role of the WTO. (AO1, AO2, AO3)   5 marks

....

....

....

....

18 With reference to Figure 3 above, complete the following table to show how the
market share in world exports changed from 1985 to 2008. (AO1, AO2)   4 marks

	2008 (% of world exports)	1985 (% of world exports)
USA		
China		
Germany		
UK		

19 With reference to the data in your completed table, examine TWO reasons for the change in the pattern of global trade. (AO1, AO2, AO3, AO4)   `8 marks`

....

....

....

....

....

....

....

....

....

20 Define, and give an example of, the following types of trade bloc. (AO1, AO2)   `8 marks`

Trade bloc	Definition	Example
Free trade area		
Customs union		
Common market		
Monetary union		

21 With the use of a diagram explain what is meant by the following. (AO1, AO2, AO3)   `10 marks`

Trade creation	Trade diversion
Definition	Definition
Diagram	Diagram

Foreign direct investment

Foreign direct investment (FDI) is an international capital movement. This occurs when a foreign company sets up or purchases a significant share in a company in another country, so the term includes mergers and acquisitions (M and A), investment into new projects and the expansion of existing ones.

FDI has three usual strategic aims: horizontal, such as Nissan assembling cars in Japan and the UK; vertical, such as Tata, which produces steel and owns various car brands including Jaguar and Land Rover; and conglomerate, such as Alphabet, which manages Google and Google Capital, an investment fund.

㉒ Define the following terms:

a **multinational business (MNC) (AO1)**   `1 mark`

....

....

b **outsourcing (AO1)**   `1 mark`

....

....

㉓ Evaluate the benefits for an economy of your choice of an increase in inward foreign investment from large multinational companies. (AO1, AO2, AO3, AO4) `25 marks`

Use the table below to help you plan your answer, and then write your essay on a separate sheet of paper. Aim to include at least three analysis and evaluation points.

Point/knowledge (AO1 4 marks)	Analysis (AO3 8 marks)	Application (AO2 4 marks)	Evaluation (AO4 9 marks)
Read the question; make sure your points are relevant; define economic concepts	Use of economic concepts; explained, annotated and labelled diagrams; use of logical chains of reasoning	Integrated supporting evidence from the extract, your own examples and the context of the question	Arguments for and against; significance of arguments; reference to context and evidence; a justified conclusion that considers the question as a whole, not just one part

24 Draw an aggregate demand and supply diagram to show the impact of a rise in FDI. (AO1, AO2)

4 marks

Balance of payments

In Theme 2, you covered the components of the balance of payments and the reasons for the UK running a current account deficit. You should remember that the balance of payments records all financial transactions between one country and the rest of the world and the separate accounts must balance so their sum is equal to zero.

25 Using research and your own knowledge, complete the table below to show the different sub-accounts of the current and financial accounts, an example of the transaction and the UK balance. (AO1, AO2)

24 marks

Current account: this records transactions — primarily the movements of all goods and services into and out of the UK, but also primary and secondary income		
Sub-accounts	**Example of transaction**	**UK balance**
1		
2		
3		
4		

Financial account: this comprises transactions associated with changes of ownership of the UK's foreign financial assets and liabilities		
Sub-accounts	**Example**	**UK balance**
1		
2		
3		
4		

Causes of current account imbalances

Global imbalances, or current account deficits and surpluses, are often seen as a problem and a contributing factor to the financial crisis. The UK has recorded a current account deficit in every year since 1984 while the USA last had a current account surplus in 1991. By contrast, China was the world's largest surplus country, reaching over 10% of GDP in 2007.

Tensions between the USA and China about who was the principal cause of this imbalance have led to scrutiny of the value of the Chinese Renminbi and the impact of China's growing financial reserves.

26 Examine TWO possible causes of a trade in goods deficit on the current account. (AO1, AO2, AO3, AO4)

8 marks

27 Examine TWO consequences for the US economy of financial account capital inflows from China. (AO1, AO2, AO3, AO4)

8 marks

28 To what extent are large trade imbalances a concern? (AO1, AO2, AO3, AO4)

15 marks

Write your answer on a separate sheet of paper.

Policies to correct imbalances

Correcting global trade imbalances means that spending must be transferred from trade-deficit countries, such as the USA and UK, to trade-surplus countries, such as China and Germany. Some imbalances may be self-correcting through their impact on business cycles and floating exchange rates.

29 Explain the impact of a trade deficit on a country's exchange rate. Use a supply and demand diagram in your answer. (AO1, AO2, AO3)   `5 marks`

30 Explain ONE way in which expenditure-reducing policies could reduce a country's deficit on its trade in goods balance. (AO1, AO2, AO3)   `5 marks`

31 Assess the use of expenditure-switching policies as a way of reducing trade deficits. (AO1, AO2, AO3, AO4)   `10 marks`

Write your answer on a separate sheet of paper.

Competitiveness

The World Economic Forum produces an annual competitiveness report. It defines 'competitiveness' as 'the set of institutions, policies, and factors that determine the level of productivity of a country'.

32 Define the following two measures of competitiveness:

a   unit labour costs (AO1)   `2 marks`

b   real exchange rate (AO1)   `2 marks`

15

33 Evaluate the measures which could be pursued by individual firms and by the government to improve competitiveness. (AO1, AO2, AO3, AO4) `12 marks`

Write your answer on a separate sheet of paper.

34 Assess the economic impact on a country of your choice of a reduction in its international competitiveness. (AO1, AO2, AO3, AO4) `25 marks`

Use the table below to help you plan your answer, and then write your essay on a separate sheet of paper. Aim to include at least three analysis and evaluation points.

Point/knowledge (AO1 4 marks)	Analysis (AO3 8 marks)	Application (AO2 4 marks)	Evaluation (AO4 9 marks)
Read the question; make sure your points are relevant; define economic concepts	Use of economic concepts; explained, annotated and labelled diagrams; use of logical chains of reasoning	Integrated supporting evidence from the extract, your own examples and the context of the question	Arguments for and against; significance of arguments; reference to context and evidence; a justified conclusion that considers the question as a whole, not just one part

Fixed and floating exchange rates

The value of a floating exchange rate — the price of one currency in terms of another — is determined through the interaction of demand and supply in the foreign exchange market. Fixed exchange rates are most likely to be soft exchange rate pegs — currencies that maintain a stable value against an anchor currency or a composite of currencies. The exchange rate can be pegged to the anchor within a narrow (+/–1%) or a wide (up to +/–30%) range. China is an example of this type of system. Countries face a 'trilemma': they must choose between free capital flows, a fixed exchange rate and an autonomous monetary policy.

35 Define the following terms:

a effective exchange rate (AO1) `2 marks`

....

....

b   Marshall–Lerner condition (AO1)

2 marks

....

....

c   J-curve effect (AO1)

2 marks

....

....

36 Explain ONE mechanism by which a government or central bank could cause a devaluation in its exchange rate. Use a supply and demand diagram in your answer. (AO1, AO2, AO3)

5 marks

....

....

....

37 Apart from changes in UK interest rates, examine TWO possible factors which have led to changes in the value of the pound sterling against the US dollar. (AO1, AO2, AO3, AO4)

8 marks

....

....

....

....

....

....

....

....

....

....

....

38 Evaluate the impact on the UK economy of a depreciation in the pound sterling against the euro. (AO1, AO2, AO3, AO4)

12 marks

Write your answer on a separate sheet of paper.

Single currencies

Although there are several single currency zones in operation, such as the Central African Franc in the West African Economic and Monetary Union (UEMOA), the focus tends to be on Economic and Monetary Union (EMU) in Europe. Monetary policy is set by the European Central Bank (ECB) to target the average inflation rate for all Eurozone members.

39 Maastricht criteria must be passed before the euro can be adopted. Outline the following convergence criteria. (AO2)

5 marks

Inflation	
Government finances	**Budget deficit:**
	National debt:
Exchange rate	
Interest rate	

40 Assess the likely economic effects for a country choosing to leave the Eurozone. (AO1, AO2, AO3, AO4)

15 marks

Write your answer on a separate sheet of paper.

Exam-style questions (data response)

Read Extracts 1 and 2 and then answer the questions that follow on a separate sheet of paper.

Extract 1: The Mexican peso crisis

The increasing international integration of financial markets in the past few decades has brought many advantages, such as a more efficient allocation of global savings, and so greater investment and growth. But since 1982, emerging markets have suffered three financial crises. The most recent was the Asian Financial Crisis in 1997, when currencies and real estate and equity prices fell throughout Asia as capital fled from countries once favoured by investors. Increased integration into the global economy has meant emerging economies are more exposed to large capital outflows and shocks to one country can be spread more quickly to others.

When Mexico joined the North American Free Trade Association (NAFTA) in 1994, its current account deficit was already at 6½% of GDP due to a rapid appreciation of the peso and a fall in the savings ratio. Mexico's weak external position was further weakened by political problems after elections and a sudden rise in US interest rates. This caused international investors to withdraw some investments, amid uncertainty about Mexico's ability to service its government debt, which was indexed to the dollar, and domestic banks' ability to recover unwise loans. Confidence did not return until the IMF approved over $17 billion in credit and designed an adjustment programme.

Source: adapted from 'Financial crises in emerging economies', *IMF Finance & Development*, December 1998

Extract 2: Mercosur

Mercosur is a customs union in South America, making up more than three-quarters of the region's economic activity and with four members, Argentina, Brazil, Paraguay and Uruguay. Argentina has suggested they advance towards a monetary union and introduce a common currency, the Gaucho. To develop into an optimum currency area, the countries must increase their level of integration so that capital and labour can flow more easily across borders. The Eurozone has proved that to have a sustainable currency union, there must be fiscal integration to absorb and smooth economic shocks.

1. Explain one similarity and one difference between a free trade area, such as NAFTA, and a customs unions, such as Mercosur. (AO1, AO2, AO3) `5 marks` (6)

2. With reference to Extract 1, analyse the reasons for Mexico's deteriorating current account situation. (AO1, AO2, AO3, AO4) `8 marks` (10)

3. Assess the possible macroeconomic effects on a country of a shock such as the Mexican peso crisis. (AO1, AO2, AO3, AO4) `10 marks` (12)

4. Evaluate the motives for multinational companies choosing to invest into countries that are part of Mercosur. (AO1, AO2, AO3, AO4) `12 marks` (14)

5. Examine the policies the Mexican government could use to reduce its current account deficit. (AO1, AO2, AO3, AO4) `15 marks` (18)

Exam-style questions (essay)

6. Assess the advantages and disadvantages for a country inside the European Union of choosing to adopt the euro as its currency. (AO1, AO2, AO3, AO4) `25 marks` (30)

Use the table below to help you plan your answer, and then write your essay on a separate sheet of paper. Aim to include at least three analysis and evaluation points.

Point/knowledge (AO1 4 marks)	Analysis (AO3 8 marks)	Application (AO2 4 marks)	Evaluation (AO4 9 marks)
Read the question; make sure your points are relevant; define economic concepts	Use of economic concepts; explained, annotated and labelled diagrams; use of logical chains of reasoning	Integrated supporting evidence from the extract, your own examples and the context of the question	Arguments for and against; significance of arguments; reference to context and evidence; a justified conclusion that considers the question as a whole, not just one part

Poverty and inequality

Measuring poverty and inequality

Income and wealth inequality can be measured in different ways, one of the key distinctions being between or within countries. In 1990, nearly half of the population in the developing world lived on less than $1.25 a day; that proportion had dropped to 14% by 2015. Rapid economic growth during the past 30 years has lifted millions of citizens out of poverty, but progress has been uneven between countries and regions. In 2011, nearly 60% of the world's 1 billion extremely poor people lived in just five countries and one in five people in developing regions still live on less than $1.25 a day.

Goal 1 of the Sustainable Development Goals is to eradicate extreme poverty everywhere by 2030. Globally, many countries have seen rising income inequality and have their own national poverty lines, which aim to show **relative poverty**.

A Lorenz curve is a measure of inequality. It shows the population along the horizontal axis, from the poorest to the richest, and the fraction of total income that a given proportion of the population has on the vertical axis.

1 Define the following types of poverty measure. (AO1, AO2)   8 marks

Poverty type	Definition and measure
Absolute poverty	
Relative poverty	
Multidimensional poverty index (MPI)	
HPI-1 (for developing countries)	

2 Draw a Lorenz curve diagram showing a line of perfect equality and an economy that has 80 employees who receive 60% of the national income, their 10 employers who earn 40% of the national income, and 10 unemployed people who have no income. (AO1, AO2, AO3)   5 marks

Table 1 UK disposable income 2012/13 by decile

	Decile groups of all households ranked by disposable income									
	Bottom	2nd	3rd	4th	5th	6th	7th	8th	9th	10th
% of total income	3.0	4.8	5.7	6.7	7.6	8.8	10.2	12.0	15.0	26.2

(Source: ONS)

3 a Using the data in Table 1, draw and label a Lorenz curve diagram below. (AO2)   3 marks

21

b Explain how the Gini coefficient is measured. (AO1) `2 marks`

....

....

Causes of poverty and inequality

Greater inequality can occur because the richest are getting wealthier, or the poorest are being paid less, or a combination of the two. Weak income growth in the poorest quintiles of society has been linked to the rise of globalisation, institutional changes, technological progress and social norms. For example, offshoring of manufacturing and low-skill service sector jobs to emerging economies and increased international wage competition are linked to globalisation. Institutional changes, such as deregulation, changes to the tax and benefit systems, and declining trade union membership, have reduced wage bargaining power and income redistribution. Links between political power and the rich may exacerbate this situation. Technological change, meaning greater automation of low-skill jobs and increasing demand for highly educated workers, is another potential cause. Social norms may also play a part, where gaps between workers and company directors are tolerated and perhaps justified as fair reward for the most skilled.

④ What is the difference between wealth and income? (AO1) `2 marks`

....

....

⑤ Explain what is meant by the derived demand for labour. (AO1) `2 marks`

....

....

⑥ With the use of a labour supply and demand diagram in each case, explain TWO possible causes of widening income inequality. (AO1, AO2, AO3) `10 marks`

Cause 1	Cause 2
Point and analysis	Point and analysis
Labour market diagram	Labour market diagram

Policies to reduce income and wealth inequalities

In economics, the allocation of scarce resources is always portrayed as a choice between the efficiency of markets and equitable distribution through government intervention. Inequality tends to be the result of an unconstrained market mechanism and redistribution can be inefficient, as incentives to work and invest are reduced, and the administrative costs of tax and other interventions reduce the resources transferred. However, high inequality might damage sustainable growth. It might increase the risks of crises, limit fiscal options, and deny the poor opportunities to invest in human capital and enterprise.

In advanced economies, fiscal policy is an effective way of reducing income inequality. Progressive direct taxation and public expenditure, through transfer payments, such as public pensions, and universal access to public healthcare and education have all helped to redistribute incomes. However, redistribution in advanced economies is becoming harder in the face of rising national debt, expenditure cuts and pressure to cut welfare spending.

In developing economies, tax revenue is limited due to small tax bases, tax loopholes, large informal economies and poor tax compliance. This means redistribution through progressive tax and public spending is much harder to achieve.

7 **With the use of a labour market diagram, examine the likely impact on income distribution of an increase in the national minimum wage. (AO1, AO2, AO3, AO4)** `8 marks`

....

....

....

....

....

8 **With reference to both direct and indirect taxes, explain what is meant by progressive and regressive taxation. (AO1, AO2, AO3)** `5 marks`

....

....

....

....

....

Exam-style questions (data response)

Look at the data in Table 2 and Figure 4, then answer the questions that follow on a separate sheet of paper.

Table 2 Selected development indicators

Country	Angola	Botswana	Niger	Nigeria
GDP per capita (PPP)	7,016	16,035	1,048	6,031
Investment (% GDP)	14.8	30.1	38.4	15.1
Economic growth	4.2	4.9	6.9	6.3
HDI (2014)	0.526	0.683	0.504	0.337
% population living below $1.25 a day (PPP 2002–12)			43.6	68.0
Gini coefficient	42.66	n.a.	34.55	48.83

Sources: IMF, *World Economic Outlook*, April 2015; World Bank; UN, *Human Development Reports*

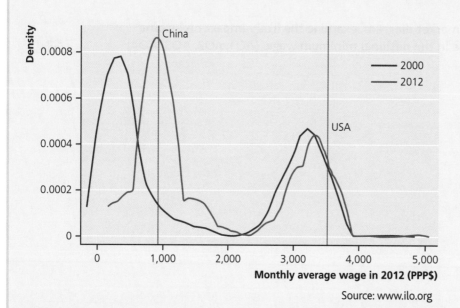

Figure 4 Global monthly average wage distribution in 2000 and 2012 (2012 PPP$)

1 With reference to Table 2, explain the difference between HDI and absolute poverty. (AO1, AO2, AO3) **5 marks** **6**

2 With reference to Table 2 and the ratio of gross fixed capital formation to GDP, examine the correlation between higher levels of investment and annual GDP growth. (AO1, AO2, AO3, AO4) **8 marks** **10**

3 With reference to Figure 4, discuss the role globalisation has played in changing the global monthly average wage distribution. (AO1, AO2, AO3, AO4) **12 marks** **14**

4 Assess the view that inequality is inevitable in free market economies. (AO1, AO2, AO3, AO4) **10 marks** **12**

5 Discuss the economic effects of rising levels of income inequality. (AO1, AO2, AO3, AO4) **15 marks** **18**

Exam-style questions (essay)

6 Evaluate the effectiveness of fiscal policy as a solution to the causes of income inequality. Refer to a developed country of your choice in your answer. (AO1, AO2, AO3, AO4)

25 marks **30**

Use the table below to help you plan your answer, and then write your essay on a separate sheet of paper. Aim to include at least three analysis and evaluation points.

Point/knowledge (AO1 4 marks)	Analysis (AO3 8 marks)	Application (AO2 4 marks)	Evaluation (AO4 9 marks)
Read the question; make sure your points are relevant; define economic concepts	Use of economic concepts; explained, annotated and labelled diagrams; use of logical chains of reasoning	Integrated supporting evidence from the extract, your own examples and the context of the question	Arguments for and against; significance of arguments; reference to context and evidence; a justified conclusion that considers the question as a whole, not just one part

Topic 3

Emerging and developing economies

Economic growth and development

Economic growth and living standards are topics that were covered in Theme 2 and it is vital you remember that growth is not the same as development.

China has achieved rapid economic growth since economic reforms started in 1978 under Deng Xiaoping. Economic growth has averaged 9.8% per annum since 1978 and the proceeds of greater output should 'trickle down' to the rest of the country. At purchasing power parity, gross domestic product per head has risen almost tenfold, lifting around 660 million out of

absolute poverty. The redistribution of higher incomes through better public services can help achieve further development.

However, rapid economic growth has led to pressures on the environment. China's 13th Five-Year Plan acknowledges this problem and targets a lower 6.5% growth rate (down from 7%), as well as relaxing family-planning policy to allow families to have two children, and reforming inefficient state-owned enterprises by improving competition in monopolised sectors.

1 **With reference to your own knowledge of the UK economy and using an aggregate demand and supply diagram in each case, explain what happened to the UK's actual and potential rate of economic growth. (AO1, AO2, AO3)** `10 marks`

Actual growth	Potential growth
Definition	Definition
Diagram	Diagram

2 Explain how economic growth can 'trickle down' and lead to greater development. (AO1, AO2, AO3)

5 marks

....

....

....

....

3 With reference to China, assess the arguments for choosing to target a slower rate of economic growth. (AO1, AO2, AO3, AO4)

10 marks

Write your answer on a separate sheet of paper.

Harrod–Domar and Lewis model

After the experiences of the Marshall Plan, when huge amounts of US assistance were given to help rebuild the economies devastated by the Second World War, economists became more interested in development models. Four main approaches emerged:

- models viewing development as occurring through linear stages (e.g. Rostow and Harrod–Domar)
- models viewing development as an internal process of structural change (e.g. Lewis two-sector model)
- models viewing development as a process of international dependence (such as the unequal international power between the centre and periphery)
- neoclassical approaches which emphasised the benefits of free markets

In Theme 1, you will have drawn a *PPF* diagram to show that an economy which produces fewer consumer goods is able to produce more capital goods. In Theme 2 you learned about the circular flow of income, and how planned injections equal planned withdrawals, and more specifically that saving equals investment. This basic analysis suggests that less consumption (fewer consumer goods) means more saving, which in turn means greater investment, and as long as gross investment is greater than depreciation, this will lead to faster rates of economic growth.

The Harrod–Domar model says the rate of change of income (economic growth) is determined by the savings rate (s) divided by the capital–output ratio (k: the amount of output a unit of capital will produce).

4 Explain what is meant by a savings gap. (AO1, AO2, AO3)

5 marks

....

....

....

....

5 Explain why savings are likely to be low in developing countries. (AO1, AO2, AO3)

5 marks

....

....

....

....

6 In the space below, draw a *PPF* diagram with the axes labelled 'Consumer goods' and 'Capital goods', and annotate it to show the following: (AO1) **5 marks**

   a Point *X* where resources are equally allocated to consumer and capital goods

   b Point *A* where there is a higher rate of saving

   c A new *PPF* to show the impact of *A* on the output of both consumer and capital goods in the future

   d A new *PPF* to show the impact of choosing to be at *A* and the additional impact of a fall in the capital–output ratio (improved technology)

7 Explain why higher rates of saving may not lead to higher rates of economic growth. (AO1, AO2, AO3) **5 marks**

8 Explain, with reference to the Lewis two-sector model and the law of diminishing marginal returns, why extra workers in agriculture might lead to a marginal product of labour in agriculture equal to zero. (AO1, AO2, AO3) **5 marks**

9 Assess, with reference to China, the role migration from rural agriculture to urban manufacturing has played in increasing development. (AO1, AO2, AO3, AO4) **10 marks**

Write your answer on a separate sheet of paper.

Aid

Aid is a transfer of resources, either as cash or in the form of commodities or service, to developing countries with the principal aim of promoting development. It must be given under concessional terms, and so can be a grant, which is not repaid, or a loan. Microfinance provides very small loans at affordable rates to allow people to start their own businesses. However, the rapid and unregulated growth in private, profit-seeking, microcredit industries has been blamed for excessive rates of interest and high-risk lending.

The Millennium Development Goals (MDGs) established measurable, universally agreed objectives for eradicating extreme poverty and hunger, preventing deadly but treatable disease, and expanding educational opportunities to all children, among other development imperatives. The 17 new Sustainable Development Goals (SDGs) will guide policy and funding for the next 15 years, beginning with a historic pledge to end poverty. The Department for International Development (DFID) leads the UK's work to end extreme poverty. It aims to end the need for aid by creating jobs, unlocking the potential of girls and women and helping to save lives when humanitarian emergencies hit.

10 Define, and give an example of, the following different types of aid: (AO1, AO2) **8 marks**

Term	Definition	Example
Bilateral aid		
Multilateral aid		
Tied aid		
Concessional loan		

11 Research the four largest donors and recipients of official development assistance (ODA) in recent years and complete the table below. (AO2) **4 marks**

	Largest ODA donors ($bn)	Largest ODA recipients ($bn)
1		
2		
3		
4		

12 Explain how an expansion of microfinance schemes could promote development. (AO1, AO3)

6 marks

Point	Linked development
1	
2	
3	

13 Discuss the likely costs and benefits of increasing aid flows as a means to improve development. (AO1, AO2, AO3, AO4)

15 marks

Write your answer on a separate sheet of paper.

Debt relief and the role of the World Bank and IMF

The International Monetary Fund (IMF) and the International Development Association (IDA), part of the World Bank, have a variety of objectives but have three main areas of collaboration:

- Heavily Indebted Poor Countries (HIPC) Initiative
- Multilateral Debt Relief Initiative (MDRI)
- Poverty Reduction Strategy Papers (PRSP), introduced in 1999, whereby countries must draw up their own strategies for reducing poverty

The majority of debt is owed to large creditors, such as the World Bank, the African Development Bank, the IMF and governments, but some is also owed to commercial creditors too.

The arguments in favour of debt relief are similar to those in favour of aid, and focus on the opportunity cost of servicing the debt, which can reach over 75% of public expenditure in some countries. The failure of many poor countries to close the gap on industrial countries before the mid-1980s was seen as a justification for expanding the role of the market in developing countries. Loans from the IMF and World Bank became conditional on economic reforms, and before PRSP, the IMF enforced 'Stabilisation Policies' and the World Bank 'Structural Adjustment Policies'.

14 Define what is meant by 'debt forgiveness'. (AO1)

2 marks

15 Explain the following two arguments against debt relief:

a moral hazard (AO1, AO3)

2 marks

b corruption (AO1, AO3)

2 marks

16 Explain three ways in which debt forgiveness might promote development. (AO1, AO3)

6 marks

Point	Linked development
1	
2	
3	

17 Using your own research, explain the role of the World Bank. (AO1, AO2, AO3)

5 marks

....
....
....
....
....

18 Using your own research, explain the role of the IMF. (AO1, AO2, AO3)

5 marks

....
....
....
....
....

19 Using your own research and knowledge of a developing country of your choice, discuss whether increasing the role of the market will raise the rate of economic growth. (AO1, AO2, AO3, AO4)

12 marks

Write your answer on a separate sheet of paper

Primary product dependency, buffer stock schemes and fair trade

Prebisch and **Singer** developed a hypothesis which stated that the terms of trade between primary product exports and manufactured goods imports would worsen over time. There are further problems attached to being resource rich, such as the increased risks of corruption and conflict, and a lack of access to export markets, because many developed countries subsidise and protect their farmers, as in the case of US cotton farmers and the EU's Common Agricultural Policy.

Another problem is known as Dutch disease. This occurs when there is a large inflow of foreign currency — often as a result of a rise in commodity prices, but also from a surge in foreign aid and FDI. The term was coined after the Netherlands discovered valuable natural gas reserves in the North Sea in the 1960s.

20 In each case below, give an example of a specific commodity and a country that produces it.

a Soft commodity (AO1, AO2)　　　　　　　　　　　　　　　　　　2 marks

....

....

b Hard commodity (AO1, AO2)　　　　　　　　　　　　　　　　　　2 marks

....

....

21 a Why do commodity prices fluctuate so much? Use a supply and demand diagram in your answer. (AO1, AO2, AO3)　　　5 marks

....

....

....

....

....

b What is the impact on households, firms and the government of commodity price volatility in primary product dependent countries? (AO1, AO2, AO3)　　　5 marks

....

....

....

....

22 Answer the following two questions in relation to the Prebisch and Singer hypothesis.

a Why did they think the terms of trade would deteriorate? (AO1, AO2, AO3)　　　5 marks

....

....

....

....

....

b **Why might a deterioration in the terms of trade constrain growth?**
   (AO1, AO2, AO3)   5 marks

....

....

....

....

....

23 **With the use of an exchange rate diagram, and your own research, explain how**
     Colombia suffered Dutch disease due to higher coffee prices in the 1970s.
     (AO1, AO2, AO3)   8 marks

....

....

....

....

....

....

24 **Assess the case for the introduction of fair trade schemes in developing countries.**
     (AO1, AO2, AO3, AO4)   10 marks

Write your answer on a separate sheet of paper.

Population growth, corruption, property rights and other constraints

Increasing economic growth and development in developing countries is a case of both understanding what factors might promote growth and knowing what obstacles might prevent the development process occurring. It is important to remember that achieving faster rates of growth today will involve tackling issues that have not been faced by earlier industrialisers. Examples might be global warming, higher commodity prices, particularly in energy, and changing global demographics. Equally, the solutions and problems faced by countries will be unique to each, although some broad grouping is possible.

Sub-Saharan Africa has to overcome the legacy of borders drawn up under colonial rule, with some countries having no access to the sea, and the problems associated with an abundance of natural resources. Of course, there are always divergences in growth performance within Africa. Botswana has grown quickly despite valuable resources, while political stability has occurred within Ghana but not its neighbour, Ivory Coast. Some middle-income countries have begun to lose their comparative advantage in low-wage industries and are struggling to expand higher-skill sectors such as services.

25 **Explain three ways in which corruption can constrain development. (AO1, AO3)**   `6 marks`

....

....

....

....

....

....

....

....

....

26 **Explain three economic consequences of rapid population growth. (AO1, AO3)**   `6 marks`

....

....

....

....

....

....

....

....

....

27 **Explain three economic consequences of insecure property rights. (AO1, AO3)**   `6 marks`

....

....

....

....

....

....

....

....

....

Exam-style questions (data response)

Read Extracts 1, 2 and 3 and answer the questions that follow on a separate sheet of paper.

Extract 1: The Growth Report: strategies for sustained growth and development

Since 1950, 13 economies have grown at an average rate of 7% or more for at least 25 years. They are a diverse range of countries in terms of size, location, natural resources and culture: Botswana, Brazil, China, Hong Kong, Indonesia, Japan, South Korea, Malaysia, Malta, Oman, Singapore, Taiwan and Thailand. There were some common features they all shared: they exploited opportunities in the world economy, and so opened up to the benefits of trade, FDI, and technology transfer; they maintained macroeconomic stability, and so encouraged private investment; they sustained high rates of saving and investment, with investment at least 25% of GDP, with 5–7% investment into infrastructure and 7–8% of GDP spent on education, training and health; they let markets allocate resources, encouraging entrepreneurship and competition; and they had committed, credible and capable government, which allowed for the equality of opportunity, particularly for women.

Source: Commission on Growth and Development, 2008

Extract 2: Infrastructure in Indonesia

Indonesia's infrastructure has struggled to keep up with its fast-growing economy and rising population. Gridlock on the roads leads to rising fuel costs and lower labour productivity, and exacerbates the problems of bulging ports. Despite the majority of Indonesian trade coming by sea, container ports suffer from years of under-investment and struggle to match the pace of development in China, Korea and Japan. Raw material imports are regularly held up, costing businesses time and money, while exports equally suffer, deterring investment from multinationals and damaging Indonesian competitiveness.

Extract 3: Angola's economic outlook, 2015

Angola's economic growth slowed to 4.5% in 2014, down from 6.8% in 2013, as a result of falling international oil prices, a temporary decline in domestic oil production and prolonged drought. Non-oil sectors were the main drivers of growth, notably agriculture, energy, manufacturing, construction and the service sector. Nonetheless, the economy remains dependent on oil, which is estimated to account for 95% of exports, 70% of total government revenue and 46% of gross domestic product (GDP). Lower oil prices are expected to lead to sizeable cuts in public spending and a consequent deceleration of GDP growth to 3.8% in 2015. Social pressures are increasing due to the high unemployment rate (26%), particularly among youth; significant poverty, affecting 36.6% of the population; and high income inequality, with a Gini coefficient of 55.3.

Source: www.africaneconomicoutlook.org

1. Explain one advantage and one disadvantage of using HDI as a measure of development. (AO1, AO2, AO3) **5 marks** 6

2. With reference to Extract 2, examine the benefits of increasing investment in infrastructure in developing economies. (AO1, AO2, AO3, AO4) **8 marks** 10

3. With reference to Extract 1, and apart from investment in infrastructure, discuss the strategies used as a means of achieving sustained growth and development. (AO1, AO2, AO3, AO4) **12 marks** 14

4. Assess the use of a buffer stock scheme as a means of reducing the fluctuations in the price of oil in Angola. Use a diagram in your answer. (AO1, AO2, AO3, AO4) **10 marks** 12

5. With reference to Extract 3, discuss the economic consequences of developing countries specialising in the export of primary products. (AO1, AO2, AO3, AO4) **15 marks** 18

Exam-style questions (essays)

6 Discuss the economic consequences of a lack of human capital in developing countries. (AO1, AO2, AO3, AO4) — **25 marks** · **30**

7 Sri Lanka's 5-year tourism strategy aims to increase tourism-related employment and foreign exchange earnings. To what extent is developing the tourist sector the most significant way to increase the rate of economic growth? (AO1, AO2, AO3, AO4) — **25 marks** · **30**

8 With reference to countries of your choice, evaluate four constraints to economic growth and development. (AO1, AO2, AO3, AO4) — **25 marks** · **30**

9 To what extent can increasing the flow of aid and granting debt relief to developing countries lead to higher levels of development? (AO1, AO2, AO3, AO4) — **25 marks** · **30**

Copy and complete the table below to help you plan your answers, and then write your essays on separate sheets of paper. Aim to include at least three analysis and evaluation points.

Point/knowledge (AO1 4 marks)	Analysis (AO3 8 marks)	Application (AO2 4 marks)	Evaluation (AO4 9 marks)
Read the question; make sure your points are relevant; define economic concepts	Use of economic concepts; explained, annotated and labelled diagrams; use of logical chains of reasoning	Integrated supporting evidence from the extract, your own examples and the context of the question	Arguments for and against; significance of arguments; reference to context and evidence; a justified conclusion that considers the question as a whole, not just one part

Topic 4

Monetary policy and the financial sector

Topic 4 links the policies covered in Theme 2 to several key topic areas in Theme 4:

- measures to improve imbalances on the current account of the balance of payments (4.1.7)
- factors and strategies influencing growth and development (4.3.2) and (4.3.3)
- the financial sector (4.4)
- the role of the state in the macroeconomy (4.5)

Role of financial markets and market failures

If the banking system is working well, its presence is hardly noticed. It is treated as part of the background infrastructure of the economy, much like the electricity grid. When the financial crisis erupted in 2008, economists and the public were suddenly more aware of the financial system and realised it was poorly understood and poorly regulated. The World Economic Forum measures financial market development as its eighth pillar of competitiveness.

1 **Explain three roles of financial markets. (AO1, AO3)**   `6 marks`

Point	Linked development
1	
2	
3	

2 **Explain three types of market failure in financial markets. (AO1, AO2, AO3)**   `9 marks`

Point	Linked development and example
1	
2	
3	

37

3 Financial markets have developed significantly in emerging markets in recent decades. Discuss the impact of financial market development on rates of economic growth. (AO1, AO2, AO3, AO4)

12 marks

Write your answer on a separate sheet of paper.

4 The UK government nationalised Northern Rock (then the country's fifth-largest mortgage lender) in February 2008. Discuss the arguments for and against government nationalisation of banks. (AO1, AO2, AO3, AO4)

15 marks

Write your answer on a separate sheet of paper.

Role of central banks

5 Explain TWO functions of a central bank. (AO1, AO2, AO3)

5 marks

6 Examine the advantages of making a central bank independent. (AO1, AO2, AO3, AO4)

8 marks

7 Examine the arguments for and against inflation targeting. (AO1, AO2, AO3, AO4)

8 marks

Monetary policy

In Theme 2, you learned how monetary policy is set by the central bank and is usually independent of the government, although its objectives are determined by the government. In the UK, the main objective of the bank's monetary policy is to target inflation at 2%, and so achieve price stability in the medium term, but it should also support the government's objectives of high employment and sustained growth.

Monetary policy is used in a similar way in other advanced economies. In the USA, the Federal Reserve sets monetary policy with the aim of achieving price stability (a 2% inflation target over the medium term), full employment and moderate long-term interest rates. In the Eurozone, the European Central Bank (ECB) sets monetary policy for the 19 members of the euro area with the aim of keeping inflation below 2%.

8 **Explain why price stability should promote economic growth. (AO1, AO2, AO3)**　　`5 marks`

....

....

....

....

....

....

....

....

....

9 **Examine the effectiveness of quantitative easing as a way of promoting economic growth. (AO1, AO2, AO3, AO4)**　　`8 marks`

....

....

....

....

....

....

....

....

....

....

....

....

....

....

Exam-style questions (data response)

Look at the data in Table 3 and read Extract 1, and then answer the questions that follow on a separate sheet of paper.

Table 3 Residential loans to individuals, 2015 Q2 Summary

Purpose of loan as % of gross advances		2014 Q2	2015 Q2
House purchase		70.10	67.71
Of which:	First-time buyers	22.06	20.66
	Buy to let	13.63	15.84
	Other	34.41	31.20
Remortgage		24.10	26.17

Source: Bank of England, 8 September 2015

Extract 1: The global monetary non-system

As 2015 ended, the world boasted few areas of robust growth. This reflects a variety of factors, including low productivity growth in most advanced countries, the debt overhang from the Great Recession, and lower commodity revenues and slower global growth damaging developing economies' export-led growth model.

Central banks in most advanced economies have tried to confront weak demand. Lower interest rates should boost investment and create jobs, but consumer debt may continue to dampen consumer demand and so reduce the real return on new investment. Central banks' attraction to unconventional monetary policy, such as quantitative easing, has been used to try and boost domestic investment and consumption but with varying results.

Greater government spending on infrastructure could also boost demand. Past infrastructure spending has not been sufficient to make up for capital depreciation, but fiscal consolidation has often been prioritised, with concerns that greater spending might lead to tax rises and reduce business confidence and therefore investment.

Potential growth in industrial countries may have fallen even before the Great Recession. Former US Treasury Secretary Larry Summers popularised the phrase 'secular stagnation' to describe weak aggregate demand caused by ageing populations that want to consume less and the increasing income share of the very rich, who have a lower marginal propensity to consume. Structural reforms to labour markets can boost productivity and output, and improve public finances in the long run, but in the short term they may be difficult to deliver politically.

Deflation is a reason to adopt pro-growth measures and to avoid the problems faced by Japan, where this led to rising real interest rates, rising real wages and a cycle of lower aggregate consumption and so lower investment. Central banks will find it difficult to boost the economy by decreasing interest rates, as they are constrained by the zero lower bound on the nominal interest rate

Source: adapted from 'The global monetary non-system' by Raghuram Rajan, 6 January 2016, Project Syndicate (www.tinyurl.com/hukzyrz)

1 With reference to Table 3, calculate the annual percentage change in the purpose of loans (as a percentage of advances) for first-time house purchases and for remortgage. (AO1, AO2, AO3)

2 Examine TWO reasons why deflation might have damaging economic effects. (AO1, AO2, AO3, AO4)

3 With reference to Table 3 and Extract 1, discuss the economic impact of monetary policy as a way of offsetting 'weak demand'. (AO1, AO2, AO3, AO4)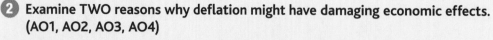

4 Assess the factors that have led to slow growth and the phrase 'secular stagnation'. (AO1, AO2, AO3, AO4) `10 marks` `12`

5 Discuss the use of fiscal and supply-side measures as a means of promoting economic growth. (AO1, AO2, AO3, AO4) `15 marks` `18`

Exam-style questions (essay)

6 To what extent have central banks been effective in addressing the consequences of the Great Recession? Refer to both monetary policy and regulatory action. (AO1, AO2, AO3, AO4) `25 marks` `30`

Use the table below to help you plan your answer, and then write your essay on a separate sheet of paper. Aim to include at least three analysis and evaluation points.

Point/knowledge (AO1 4 marks)	Analysis (AO3 8 marks)	Application (AO2 4 marks)	Evaluation (AO4 9 marks)
Read the question; make sure your points are relevant; define economic concepts	Use of economic concepts; explained, annotated and labelled diagrams; use of logical chains of reasoning	Integrated supporting evidence from the extract, your own examples and the context of the question	Arguments for and against; significance of arguments; reference to context and evidence; a justified conclusion that considers the question as a whole, not just one part

Topic 5

Role of the state in the macroeconomy

Fiscal policy: public expenditure, taxation, public sector finances

This section builds on the content of Theme 1 (indirect taxes and government intervention), Theme 2 (demand-side policies and supply-side policies) and Theme 3 (government intervention), but looks at them in a national and global context. Fiscal policy affects the level of aggregate demand but it can be used to affect supply-side performance too.

In the UK, the aim of fiscal policy had been to increase the rate of sustainable growth and create employment,

but more recently it has focused on maintaining sound public finances in the medium term. In the UK, after the apparent success of independent monetary policy, it led to the creation of the **Office for Budget Responsibility** (OBR) in 2010 to boost the credibility of the government's plans to manage public finances. The explosion of **budget deficits** and **national debt** after the financial crisis led to different fiscal policies, and increased scrutiny of them.

Public expenditure

1 With reference to a country of your choice, explain what aims fiscal policy can be used to achieve. (AO1, AO2, AO3) `5 marks`

....

....

....

....

....

....

2 Define, and give an example of, the following different types of government spending. (AO1, AO2) `6 marks`

Term	Definition	Example
Current expenditure		
Capital expenditure		
Transfer payments		

3 With reference to a country of your choice, research the four largest areas of government expenditure today and before the Great Recession of 2008. (AO1, AO2, AO3) `5 marks`

	Government spending (pre-2008)	Government spending (post-2008)
	Country/year:	Country/year:
1		
2		
3		
4		

4 With reference to the country chosen in question 3, evaluate the macroeconomic effects of a fall in the share of public expenditure as a proportion of GDP. (AO1, AO2 AO3, AO4) `15 marks`

Write your answer on a separate sheet of paper.

Taxation

5 Define and give one example of each of the following types of taxation. (AO1, AO2) `4 marks`

Term	Definition	Example
Direct taxation		
Indirect taxation		

6 With reference to a country of your choice, research the level of VAT, income tax and corporation tax before and after the Great Recession of 2008. (AO1, AO2, AO3) `5 marks`

	Country/year pre-2008:	Country/year post-2008:
VAT		
Income tax (top rate)		
Corporation tax (top rate)		

7 With reference to the country chosen above, assess TWO macroeconomic effects of an increase in the level of indirect and direct taxation. (AO1, AO2, AO3, AO4) `10 marks`

Write your answer on a separate sheet of paper.

Public sector finances

8 Outline the role of the OBR in the UK. (AO1)

....

....

9 Define the following terms. (AO1)

6 marks

Term	Definition
Budget deficit	
National debt	
Trade deficit	

10 Explain the difference between discretionary fiscal policy and automatic stabilisers. (AO1, AO2, AO3)

5 marks

....

....

....

....

....

....

11 Discuss the arguments in favour of aiming to achieve a budget surplus in the UK from 2019/20. (AO1, AO2, AO3, AO4)

12 marks

....

....

....

....

....

....

....

....

....

....

....

....

....

....

....

Supply-side policies

The main aim of supply-side policies is to improve the productive potential of the economy (and so shift long-run aggregate supply to the right). The overall result should be a higher sustainable rate of growth for the economy, without a rise in inflation, and thereby higher living standards. In practice, supply-side policies are often microeconomic policies since they aim to make labour, product and capital markets operate more efficiently.

⑫ Discuss the use of supply-side policies as a way to increase economic growth. (AO1, AO2, AO3, AO4) `12 marks`

....

....

....

....

....

....

....

....

....

....

....

....

....

⑬ Discuss whether market-oriented or government interventionist supply-side policies are more effective at increasing the rate of economic growth. (AO1, AO2, AO3, AO4) `12 marks`

Write your answer on a separate sheet of paper.

Macroeconomic policies in a global context

⑭ Measured in value and volume terms, world trade has been falling. By the end of 2015, on average G20 exports had fallen 4.5% since world trade peaked in value in October 2014. Discuss the economic impact of a fall in the value of world trade. (AO1, AO2, AO3, AO4) `15 marks`

Write your answer on a separate sheet of paper.

⑮ In 2020, the UK's corporation tax will fall to 17%. This moves the UK closer to the 12.5% rate in Ireland. Discuss the economic impact on the UK economy of this tax cut. (AO1, AO2, AO3, AO4) `15 marks`

Write your answer on a separate sheet of paper.

Exam-style questions (data response)

Look at the data in Table 4 and read Extract 1, and then answer the questions that follow on a separate sheet of paper.

Table 4 Fiscal balance, debt and growth in selected countries

Country	Fiscal overall balance (% of GDP)		General government debt (% of GDP)		Economic growth (% change)	
	2009	2014	2009	2014	2009	2014
USA	−13.5	−5.3	86.0	104.8	−3.5	2.4
Japan	−10.4	−7.7	210.2	246.4	−6.3	0.0
Germany	−3.0	0.6	72.4	73.1	−5.1	1.6
UK	−10.8	−5.7	65.8	89.5	−4.9	2.9
China	−1.8	−1.1	35.8	41.1	9.2	7.3
India	−9.8	−7.1	72.5	65.0	6.8	7.3

Source: IMF

Extract 1: Fiscal developments and economic outlook

A moderate and uneven recovery is taking place in advanced economies, supported by lower oil prices, continued accommodative monetary policy, and slower fiscal adjustment. However, high public and private debt levels continue to pose headwinds to growth and debt sustainability in some advanced economies. In addition, inflation is below target by a large margin in many countries, making the task of reducing high public debt levels more difficult. Growth in emerging market economies is softening, and financial and exchange rate volatility has increased public financing costs for some of them. Meanwhile, lower oil and commodity revenues have created challenges for exporting countries.

Although continued support from monetary policy is welcome, decisive action is also needed on fiscal policy and structural reforms. Fiscal policy can seek to stabilise output in two ways. One way is through so-called automatic stabilisers. Another way is through deliberate fiscal policy measures adopted in response to specific shocks. Automatic stabilisers are timely, but often have adverse side effects for efficiency (such as high marginal tax rates or overly generous transfers that undermine incentives to find work or create jobs).

Source: adapted from IMF, *Fiscal Monitor*, April 2015

1 With reference to Table 4, create an index of the level of UK general government debt as a percentage of GDP with 2009 as the base year. (AO1, AO2, AO3)

2 With reference to Table 4, examine TWO reasons for the differing levels of overall fiscal balance between countries. (AO1, AO2, AO3, AO4)

3 With reference to Table 4, discuss the likely economic impact of measures which a government could take to reduce an economy's national debt. (AO1, AO2, AO3, AO4)

4 Assess the use of fiscal policy as a means of stabilising output. (AO1, AO2, AO3, AO4)

5 Discuss the macroeconomic impact on the global economy of lower oil prices. (AO1, AO2, AO3, AO4) 15 marks 8

Exam-style questions (essays)

6 To what extent have policy makers learned from the 1930s in their response to the Great Recession? (AO1, AO2, AO3, AO4)   25 marks   30

7 Evaluate which of the economic ideas of Smith, Keynes and Marx is most relevant in today's economy. (AO1, AO2, AO3, AO4) 25 marks   30

Copy and complete the table below to help you plan your answers, and then write your essays on separate sheets of paper. Aim to include at least three analysis and evaluation points.

Point/knowledge (AO1 4 marks)	Analysis (AO3 8 marks)	Application (AO2 4 marks)	Evaluation (AO4 9 marks)
Read the question; make sure your points are relevant; define economic concepts	Use of economic concepts; explained, annotated and labelled diagrams; use of logical chains of reasoning	Integrated supporting evidence from the extract, your own examples and the context of the question	Arguments for and against; significance of arguments; reference to context and evidence; a justified conclusion that considers the question as a whole, not just one part

Also available

...and many more

Go to http://www.hoddereducation.co.uk/studentworkbooks for details of all our student workbooks.

Hodder Education, an Hachette UK company, Blenheim Court, George Street, Banbury, Oxfordshire OX16 5BH

Orders

Bookpoint Ltd, 130 Park Drive, Milton Park, Abingdon, Oxfordshire OX14 4SB

tel: 01235 827827

fax: 01235 400401

e-mail: education@bookpoint.co.uk

Lines are open 9.00 a.m.–5.00 p.m., Monday to Saturday, with a 24-hour message answering service.

You can also order through the Hodder Education website: www.hoddereducation.co.uk

© Sam Schmitt 2016

ISBN 978-1-4718-4460-7

First printed 2016

Impression number   5   4   3

Year   2020   2019   2018   2017

This guide has been written specifically to support students preparing for the Edexcel A-level Economics examinations. The content has been neither approved nor endorsed by Edexcel and remains the sole responsibility of the authors.

Typeset by Aptara, India

Printed in Dubai

Hachette UK's policy is to use papers that are natural, renewable and recyclable products and made from wood grown in sustainable forests. The logging and manufacturing processes are expected to conform to the environmental regulations of the country of origin.

ISBN 978-1-4718-4460-7

48

Edexcel

A LEVEL YEAR 2

WORKBOOK

Economics A

Theme 4 A global perspective

Sam Schmitt

Contents

WORKBOOK

1 **This workbook will help you** to prepare for Edexcel Economics Theme 4 A global perspective.

2 **Theme 4** could be assessed in:
- A-level paper 2 which lasts 2 hours and covers Themes 2 and 4. Section A is a set of compulsory multiple-choice and short-answer questions. Section B comprises one data-response question and in Section C there is a choice of two essays.
- A-level paper 3 which lasts 2 hours and covers all themes. Sections A and B are both compulsory data-response questions with a choice of two 25-mark essays.

3 **For each topic** in Theme 4 there are:
- stimulus materials, including key terms and concepts
- short-answer questions that build up to exam-style questions
- spaces for you to write or plan your answers
- questions which test your mathematical skills

4 **Answering the questions** will help you to build your skills and meet the assessment objectives AO1 (knowledge and understanding), AO2 (application), AO3 (analysis) and AO4 (evaluation). Quantitative skills will make up a minimum of 20% of the total marks across the A-level.

5 **You still need to** read your textbook and refer to your revision guides and lesson notes.

6 **Marks available** are indicated for all questions so that you can gauge the level of detail required in your answers.

7 **Timings** are given for the exam-style questions to make your practice as realistic as possible.

8 **Answers** are available at: www.hoddereducation.co.uk/workbookanswers.